D1630230

God's Stories
The Beginning

For Children of All Ages

Ginny Lowe, Author

Cathy Rowe, Illustrator

DEDICATION

*This book is dedicated to my
parents – Joel and Dolores Glenn,
who loved me well
and taught me the things
I needed to know.*

IN THE BEGINNING 1

WHEN GOD CREATED MAN.......................................9

NOAH AND THE ARK 14

GOD'S PROMISE TO ABRAHAM..............................22

THE BIRTH OF ISAAC...31

A WIFE FOR ISAAC 37

JACOB AND ESAU 44

JOSEPH AND HIS BROTHERS....................................54

FAMINE AND PLENTY 60

JOSEPH FORGIVES 67

BABY MOSES 76

THE BURNING BUSH 82

THE TEN PLAGUES..91

LEAVING EGYPT 102

GRUMBLING IN THE DESERT..................................110

THE TEN COMMANDMENTS 119

JOSHUA AND CALEB 125

JERICHO – THE PROMISED LAND 130

GIDEON..136

SAMPSON 144

ACKNOWLEDGMENTS

SPECIAL LOVE AND HONOR
To my Father God,
To my Lord and Savior Jesus Christ,
And to my guide, the Holy Spirit.

SPECIAL THANKS
To the most patient man I know, my husband Keith, who never
stopped encouraging me throughout our 53 years of marriage
and the 30-year project of writing this book.

SPECIAL THANKS
To my friend and pastor, Barry Arnold, who made sure this
book happened and who worked hands-on (as if he had nothing
else to do) doing all the things I don't know how to do.

SPECIAL THANKS
To Cathy Rowe for putting her skills and heart into
these wonderful illustrations.

SPECIAL THANKS
To Laura Stager for her encouragement and for making sure
all the details, jots and tittles are in their proper places.

And last, but *certainly not least*,
SPECIAL THANKS
To all the children and helpers of all ages, who have
made teaching so much fun.

I LOVE YOU ALL
Ginny

IN THE BEGINNING

Genesis 1

Do you know how it happened?
Do you know how our world came to be?
Was it an accident? Just a big **KA-BOOM**?
No. If you look you can see!

It was made by a loving and thoughtful God.
Our world was planned carefully!
The earth, the sky, and you and I,
We're all part of God's plan!
In fact, the word "creation" means,
"Made by God's own hands".

Before our earth had mountains or trees,
Before the sun or stars appeared,
There was a void -- a big nothing.
Only darkness was here.

The Holy Spirit moved over the waters.
Then God began to speak,
"LET THERE BE LIGHT!"
And (clap) there was light!
And then, what do you think?

God called the light day.
The darkness He called night.
And that was just the beginning
Of that very first day and night.

On the 2nd day God made the sky.
It was big, and blue, and way up high.
On the 3rd day God spoke,
And dry land appeared.
Then plants and fruit
And vegetables were here.

And every plant, and vegetable, and tree,
Had its very own kind of seed.
And that seed could keep making
The things that we need!

Corn makes more cornstalks,
Pea pods come from peas.
The seeds from an apple
Make more apple trees!

On the 4th day of creation,
God spoke, and lights appeared in the sky.
The sun shone down
On the earth in the day,
The moon and stars
Lit up the night.

On the 5th day of creation, God spoke powerfully,
"LET THE WATERS BE FILLED WITH FISH AND LIFE!"
And God created great creatures of the sea.
Whale, and shark, and manatee!

God said, "LET THE SKY BE FILLED WITH BIRDS!"
Then all kinds of birds started flying.
He blessed the birds, and said, "FILL THE EARTH
WITH MORE AND MORE BIRDS OF YOUR KIND!"

On the 6th day of creation,
God created again.
And it was all part of His plan,
When the Lord spoke to the land.

"LET THE EARTH BRING FORTH LIVING CREATURES!"
All were made according to their kind,
Cows and horses, cats and dogs,
Monkeys, and elephants, and porcupine.
All kinds of animals that crawl on the ground,
Wild bears, and lions, and tigers crept around!

And God saw that it was good!
It was all part of His plan.
God said, "LET US CREATE SOMEONE TO BE LIKE US!"
So God created a man from the dust!

He also created the woman, and He blessed them,
"MAKE LOTS OF BABIES AND RULE THE EARTH!
RULE OVER THE ANIMALS AND THE FISH OF THE SEA!
THERE IS PLENTY TO EAT, AND IT IS ALL FREE!"

Then God looked over all He had made.
It was very good. God had finished His work.
He blessed the 7th day and said, "THIS DAY IS HOLY,
BECAUSE IT'S THE DAY I REST FROM MY WORK."

God the Holy Father, Jesus Christ the Son,
And the Holy Spirit were there at the creation!

WHEN GOD CREATED MAN
Genesis 2-3

From the dust of the ground, God made a man!
God breathed in him, and he became alive.
From the rib of that man, God made a woman!
And Adam and Eve became husband and wife.

God planted a garden, The Garden of Eden.
He told Adam and Eve, "THIS IS ALL FOR YOU!
BUT THERE IS ONE TREE THAT YOU MUST NOT EAT.
YOU WILL SURELY DIE IF YOU DO."

Now, out in the Garden there was a serpent.
The serpent was clever and wild.
He asked the woman, "Did God really say
That you cannot eat any fruit today?"

Eve told him, "Of course we can eat the fruit!
God would not tell us a lie.
There is only ONE fruit that we must not eat
If we even touch it, we will surely die."

"You won't die if you eat," the serpent told Eve,
"Your eyes will be opened, and you'll be like God!
God knows what will happen.
Just take a bite!
You'll understand good and evil,
You'll be alright."

Eve looked at the fruit, and it looked really good!
She believed the serpent's lies.
So, she took the fruit, and then she ate it.
She wanted to be wise.

Eve gave some of the fruit to her husband,
And Adam ate it too.
Then they hung their heads, and felt ashamed.
At that very moment they knew!
They knew that the words
God had spoken were true!

They saw that they were naked,
So they took fig leaves
And made clothes to cover themselves.
They hid in the trees.
What would they do?
Then they heard God calling,
"ADAM, WHERE ARE YOU?"

Adam spoke to God, and said,
"I heard you coming, and I was afraid!
I am naked, and so I hid from you.
God said, "YOU ARE NAKED?
WHO TOLD THIS TO YOU?"

"HAVE YOU EATEN THE FRUIT FROM THE TREE
THAT I COMMANDED YOU NOT TO EAT?"
Adam said, "Yes, I ate the fruit from the tree.
It was the woman who gave it to me."

Then God said to Eve, "WHAT HAVE YOU DONE?"
Eve told Him, "The serpent lied.
He said that I didn't have to obey.
So, I ate it . . . I thought it would be O.K."

Adam and Eve had to leave the garden,
The beautiful Garden of Eden.
God made them some clothes, then sent them away,
Because they decided to disobey.

But that is not the end of the story!
God loves me and you!
God loves the woman and the man,
And God has made a plan!

Jesus loves me this I know,
For the Bible tells me so!
Even when I disobey,
God has made a way!
Jesus is the way!

NOAH AND THE ARK

Genesis 6-8

Adam and Eve were sent out of the Garden
Because they did not obey.
Then the people on the earth
Became more and more wicked,
Arguing, and fighting, and doing things their own way!

But there was one man who found favor with God,
The Bible says Noah was righteous.
That meant that Noah lived his life
Doing the things that were right in God's sight.
One day God spoke to Noah and said,
"I'M GOING TO DESTROY THE EARTH WITH A FLOOD.
BUT I WILL SAVE YOU, AND YOUR FAMILY, TOO!
LISTEN CAREFULLY, THIS IS WHAT I WANT YOU TO DO."

"BUILD AN ARK, A BOAT,
MAKE IT OUT OF GOPHER WOOD.
MAKE IT FOUR HUNDRED AND FIFTY FEET LONG,
MAKE IT SEVENTY-FIVE FEET WIDE,
AND THREE STORIES HIGH.
YOU AND YOUR FAMILY WILL BE SAFE INSIDE!

"BUILD STALLS FOR ALL OF THE ANIMALS.
THE ANIMALS WILL COME TWO BY TWO,
A MALE AND FEMALE OF EACH AND EVERY KIND."
Noah didn't understand how this could be true.
But Noah did all that God commanded him to do!

Now Noah had a wife, and 3 sons.
The sons names were Shem, Ham, and Japheth.
Each of the boys had a wife.
God was going to save these eight people's lives!

They all worked together to build the Ark.
They gathered food for themselves, and the animals too!
It took a long time, and they worked very hard.
They carefully did what God commanded them to do.

When everything was ready, the animals came!
Two by two, each male and female went in!
Noah and his sons helped them into the Ark.
What a day that must have been!

Their neighbors all laughed at Noah and his sons,
"Look what that old man has done!
He's built a boat in the middle of a field!
Hey Noah, are you having fun?

"There isn't even any water out there!
That crazy old man says he talks to God!"
They laughed and made fun of Noah, day after day.
But Noah knew there was a flood on the way!
And even though it all seemed very odd,
Noah waited patiently and trusted in God.

When all the animals were safe and sound,
Noah and his family went inside.
This was the day they'd been waiting for!
Then God shut the door.

God sent the storm! It rained and poured,
For 40 days and nights!
The Ark floated -- up and down,
But Noah and his family were safe and sound.

They watched the storm, they ate, and they slept,
With the animals all around.
But Noah and his family must have wondered,
"Will the water ever go down?"

Noah sent a dove out to see
If there was any dry land.
But the dove flew back to Noah.
The dove could not find a place to land.

Again, Noah sent out the dove.
But this time do you know what the dove found?
The dove brought back an olive leaf!
This meant that the water was going down!

When Noah sent out the dove a third time,
The dove did not return!
The dove had found a home in a tree.
Noah was as happy as he could be
Because the water was going down!

Finally, the earth dried out,
Out of the ark they all came.
They decided to build an altar to God,
To thank Him, and honor God's name.

It was God who saved these eight people,
And God saved the animals too!
Now they would begin to build a new land.
God would show them what to do!

The Bible says God was pleased with Noah.
He blessed Noah, and his sons, and their wives.
He spoke to Noah and told him,
"IT'S TIME TO FILL THE EARTH WITH NEW LIFE!"

Then God put His rainbow in the sky!
A promise to all men,
That He would not destroy the earth
With water ever again!

> *Noah did all that God commanded him to do.*
> *Noah obeyed God, and I'll obey Him too!*

GOD'S PROMISE TO ABRAHAM

Genesis 12-15

A long time ago there lived a man,
We call him Father Abraham.
He is like a father because he shows me and you
How to do what God wants us to do.
His story is in the Bible and it's absolutely true!

Abraham and his family lived in tents.
He had lots of cattle, and silver, and gold.
He had a beautiful wife named Sarah.
Abraham and Sarah were both very old.

One day the Lord told Abraham,
"I WANT YOU TO LEAVE YOUR HOME.
TAKE SARAH, YOUR WIFE, AND I WILL SHOW YOU
THE PLACE WHERE I WANT YOU TO GO."

Then God made a promise to Abraham,
"I WILL MAKE YOUR NAME GREAT!
I WILL PROTECT YOU, I WILL BLESS YOU, TOO.
ALL THE FAMILIES ON EARTH
WILL BE BLESSED THROUGH YOU!"

So, Abraham took his wife and his servants,
They packed up all of their stuff.
They took tents, and animals, and food that day.
They rode on their camels, it was a long way!

They did not know where they would go,
But Abraham knew God would show them the way.
He was ready to follow God anywhere.
Abraham said "yes" to God that day!
Abraham had decided to trust and obey!

God took Abraham to the land of Canaan.
He said,
"LIFT UP YOUR EYES AND LOOK AROUND.
FOR AS FAR AS
YOUR EYES CAN SEE,
THIS LAND IS YOURS!
IT'S A GIFT FROM ME!"

Many days later, God spoke again.
He said, "ABRAHAM, DO NOT BE AFRAID!
I WILL PROTECT YOU,
AND YOUR REWARD WILL BE GREAT!"

Abraham told God, "Lord, I want a son."
So, God took Abraham outside and said,
"LOOK UP IN THE SKY, I HAVE A PLAN!
I WANT YOU TO COUNT ALL THE STARS,
IF YOU CAN!

"AS MANY AS THERE ARE STARS IN THE SKY,
THAT'S HOW MANY CHILDREN I'M GIVING TO YOU!"
And even though Abraham was very old,
He believed God's words were true!

Abraham is called the Father of Faith.
He believed God, **no matter what**!
Whatever God said, that's what Abraham would do!
But the question is,
What about you?

If God asks you to do something hard -- would you do it?
Do you believe in God?
Are you ready to trust and obey?
Will you trust Him day after day after day?
If the answer is yes, bow your head. Let's pray!

Father God, I trust in you!
I always want to say "YES" to you.
I want my heart to be faithful and true.
Because Father God, I love You!

Wherever You go, that's where I want to go!
Whatever You say, that's what I want to do!
Wherever You are, that's where I want to be!
Thank you, Lord, for loving me!

THE BIRTH OF ISAAC

Genesis 18-21

Abraham was almost 100 years old,
He sat by his tent and looked out at his land.
God had brought him here, to the land of Canaan,
And now Abraham was a very old man.

Abraham had chosen to obey the Lord,
And he knew God had blessed him generously.
God had given this land to him
For as far as his eye could see!

As Abraham looked up he saw 3 men,
It wasn't often that strangers came to visit with him.
So, he quickly got up and ran out to them.
He said, "Please stop here and rest my friends.

"We can sit in the shade of this big oak tree.
Please stay for a while and eat dinner with me!
I'll send you some water to wash your feet,
I'm going to go and prepare some meat!"

He did not know they were angels from God!
He ran to the tent and told his wife,
"Hurry Sarah! Bake some bread!
We have company for dinner!" Abraham said.

Abraham and the angels sat down for dinner.
They ate meat, and yogurt, and fresh baked bread.
They had water to drink,
And when they were finished,
One of the angels spoke up and said,
 "Where is Sarah your wife?"

"She is in the tent," Abraham answered.
Then the angel told him, "There's a reason we're here.
We are planning to come back and visit
About the same time next year.

"And when we come back you will have
A brand-new baby boy!"
Old man Abraham was amazed, then he smiled,
And he was filled with great joy!

Now Sarah was not young; she was 90 years old,
Too old to be having a baby!
She was in the tent and she heard them talking,
She laughed to herself, "Wouldn't it be funny!

"An old woman like me!
And my husband is very old too!
How could we be having a baby?
Is it possible that this could be true?"

The angel asked Abraham, "Why did Sarah laugh?
Is anything too hard for the Lord?"
"I didn't laugh," Sarah told him.
"Yes, you did laugh," the angel told them.

About the same time next year
Sarah had a beautiful baby boy!
They named him Isaac. Sarah said,
"Everyone who hears of this will laugh with me!

"Who would have thought this could happen?
Is anything too hard for the Lord?
When we were very old
God gave us a baby boy!
No. Nothing is too hard for the Lord!"

A WIFE FOR ISAAC

Genesis 24

Now Abraham was a very old man,
And the Lord had blessed him in every way.
One day he called his most trusted servant,
"Come here. I have something important to say.

"You know how I love my son, Isaac.
He is growing into such a very nice man.
Now it is time to find him a wife.
I need you to help me with my plan.

"The young women that live around here,
They don't know God, they're not right for my son.
I want you to find someone kind and good,
Someone special to love Isaac, the way a wife should.

"I'm sending you to the place I was born,
There are people there who honor God.
I know God will help you find the one
Who will be a good wife for my precious son!"

So, the servant began to prepare for the journey,
He chose 10 of Abraham's best camels and men.
And just as Abraham had told him to do,
He took wonderful gifts, and jewelry with him.

As he traveled, the servant wondered,
"How will I know the one?
How can I choose a wife for Isaac?
He's my master's son."

So, the servant knelt down and prayed,
"O Lord give me success today.
When a girl comes to draw water,
I will ask her for a drink.
And when I hear her say,
'I'll draw water for your camels too,'
Then I'll know that she's the girl You choose!"

Before he'd finished praying,
Rebekah came along.
She went down to the water,
A jar upon her shoulder.
The servant said to her,

"I'd like a drink of water."
Rebekah smiled, "OK,
I'll give you some water,"
Then he heard her say,
 "And I'll draw water for your camels, too."

The servant silently watched Rebekah
As she watered the camels, and did her work.
When the camels had finished drinking,
He gave a ring and two bracelets to her!

He went to her home, and met her family.
He told them how God had brought him to this place.
But when he told them about his master, Abraham,
Rebekah's father had a shocked look on his face!

He said, "I am Abraham's nephew,
All of us here are related to him!"
And then Rebekah's family knew,
That God had brought this servant to them.

Rebekah agreed to go home with the servant.
She asked, "Can I take my servant girls with me?"
Her father said, "OK."
So, they packed up her things.
(She didn't forget her new bracelet and rings!)

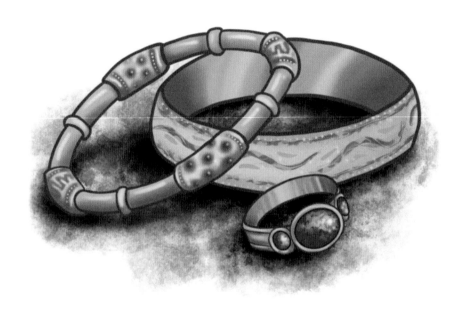

She was excited! What would it be like?
Would Isaac like her, and would he be kind?
But Rebekah knew that God was with her.
God had planned this meeting, of that she was sure!

Her parents prayed, and gave her a blessing.
Then she waved goodbye to her Mom and her Dad.
As she rode along, she must have been thinking
About the new life she now had.

Finally, they arrived, and Rebekah saw Isaac.
He was out in the field far away.
She quickly got down from her camel and asked,
"Is that him? I'd like to meet him, if I may."

And Isaac loved Rebekah.
She became his wife.
Because the servant remembered to kneel and pray
And Rebekah remembered to be extra kind.

JACOB AND ESAU

Genesis 25-27

Isaac was the son of Abraham,
And Rebekah was his wife.
They had no children, so Isaac prayed to the Lord
And God gave them twin boys that they both adored.

Esau was the oldest, he was born first.
His skin was rough and red.
He had lots of hair all over him,
But Jacob was born with soft and smooth skin.

The boys were very different from each other.
They were always ready to argue and fight.
There were problems between their father and mother,
Their family was not respectful or kind to each other.

Esau liked to be outside.
He liked to hunt animals, and bring home the meat.
His father Isaac especially loved Esau,
The meat Esau hunted was what Isaac liked to eat!

Jacob was a quiet boy,
He liked to stay home with his mom in the tent.
Rebekah loved Jacob and protected him,
Then one day something very wrong happened to them.

Esau came home from hunting, he was tired,
Jacob was cooking good things to eat.
"I'm hungry," said Esau, "I'd sure like some stew."
"OK," said Jacob, "I'll make something special for you.

"But you'll have to pay me something for my trouble."
"So, what do you want?" Esau said.
"I want the blessing that father will give when he dies."
"That's fine, I'm hungry!" Esau said.
Then Jacob gave Esau some stew and some bread.

For many years God blessed Isaac with riches and wealth.
So when Isaac was old and ready to die,
He called Esau, his firstborn son, and said,
"Esau come here and sit by my bed.

"Get your bow and arrow, and go hunt for some meat.
You know what I like, you know what to do.
When you return, I will give you my blessing.
Everything that I have will belong to you!"

So, when Esau left to hunt,
Rebekah told Jacob, "Do exactly as I say.

"Your father's blessing will be yours today!
But we must act fast. Yes, we must hurry!
We do not want Esau to get in our way.

"We will make the special food for your father.
He is almost blind, so we'll dress you like Esau.
Your father will give his blessing to you!
Once he does that, there will be nothing Esau can do.
Besides, the blessing should belong to you!
Remember? Esau traded it for your stew!"

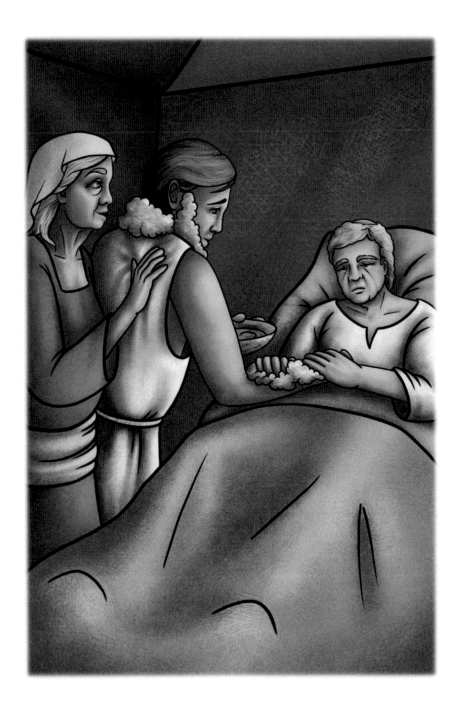

Jacob told his mother, "This will never work.
Esau has lots of hair on his skin,
If father touches me, he will know I'm not Esau.
He will know that I'm trying to trick him!"

But his mother replied, "I can fix that!
We'll put goat skin on your arms, and your neck,
        and your head.
Your father is old, he will think you are Esau."
Then Jacob and his mother did what they said.

After Isaac ate the food that Jacob had cooked,
He was ready to give Esau the blessing.
"Are you really Esau, my firstborn son?
I want to be sure that you're the right one!"

Then Jacob lied to his father.
Isaac felt the goatskin on Jacob's arms and head.
"Ahh! Yes! I can tell you are Esau,
You are my firstborn son!" Isaac said.

As soon as Isaac had finished his blessing, Esau returned from his hunt. When Esau brought his food to his father's bed, Isaac knew he'd been tricked! He cried and hung his head.

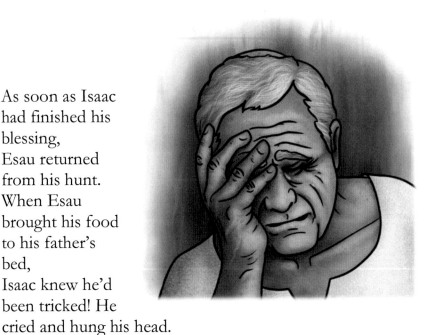

"I've given all of my riches and wealth to Jacob!
My blessing has been given, and I cannot take it back.
Jacob lied, and stole the blessing it's true,
Now there is nothing that we can do!

There is nothing left for me to give you."

The Bible says Esau was mad, He decided to kill his brother!

But their mother heard about Esau's plan,
She told Jacob, "You must leave as fast as you can!"
So, Jacob packed his bags, and away he ran!

Their story is in the Bible.
You can read how the brothers would argue and fight.
The story of Jacob and Esau,
Is the story of a family who did **not** do things right!

As you grow up, be good to your family.
Let your words always be honest, kind and true.
The Lord wants to bless you in the things that you do,
But the choice is up to you!

JOSEPH AND HIS BROTHERS
Genesis 37

Jacob and Esau were the sons of Isaac and Rebekah.
When Jacob grew up he became
The father of 12 sons and one daughter.
Dinah was his daughter's name.

Now Jacob loved his son Joseph,
He loved him more than all the rest.
He gave Joseph a coat of many colors,
Joseph thought it was special -- the very best!

Then Joseph began to have strange dreams,
And he told his dreams to his brothers.
"In my dream, you all bow down to me,"
The brothers were mad, as mad as they could be!

One day Jacob sent Joseph to find his brothers.
When the brothers saw him coming, they said,
"Here comes the dreamer who thinks he's so special,"
And they decided they wanted Joseph to be dead.

They began to make a plan to kill Joseph,
But the oldest brother, Reuben, said,
"No, let's just throw him in the well."
So they ripped off Joseph's coat, and gave him a push!
Down, down, into the well he fell!

Then the brothers sat down to eat lunch.
Judah spoke up, and said to the others,
"Maybe we should just sell Joseph as a slave,
We really should not kill our brother."

They decided to send Joseph to Egypt,
Where he would be a slave.
Joseph was only 16 years old,
And he didn't feel very brave.
But the Lord was with Joseph.

Meanwhile the brothers began to think,
"What will we tell our father?"
So, they made a plan, they killed a goat,
And put the goat's blood on Joseph's coat.

They took the coat to their father that day,
"Oh, father there's something sad we must say.
A wild animal must have taken Joseph away!"
The brothers lied to their father that day.

Their father wept, and cried out loud,
And no one could comfort him.
But the Lord was with Joseph.
Yes, the Lord God was taking care of him!

FAMINE AND PLENTY

Genesis 39–41

When Joseph was sold as a slave into Egypt,
The Lord God was with him.
He worked in the house of a man named Potiphar,
Who liked Joseph and treated him just like a friend.

Now, Potiphar had a beautiful wife,
She liked Joseph a lot.
But Joseph told her, "Stay away from me!
You have a husband, you don't need me."

This made Potiphar's wife very mad,
She made up lies about Joseph.
The soldiers came and took Joseph away,
They put him in prison and that's where he stayed.

While Joseph was in prison,
Some of the prisoners started having strange dreams.
When the men in prison told Joseph their dreams,
Joseph would tell them, "This is what your dream means."

The things Joseph told them
Always came true!
Because God was showing Joseph
What to say, and what to do!

Several years later, the Pharaoh had a dream.
He dreamed there were seven fat healthy cows.
Then seven skinny cows came out of the river,
And ate up the seven fat cows!

But when Pharaoh looked
At the cows again,
The seven skinny cows
Stayed nice and thin!

Then Pharaoh had another dream.
There were seven grains of healthy fat corn.
Then a big wind came,
And seven skinny grains
Swallowed up the seven grains
Of fat healthy corn!

Pharaoh's dreams troubled him deeply,
No one could tell him
The meaning of them.

Then, someone told Pharaoh,
"There's a man in your prison,
He can tell you your dream, because his God is with him!"

So, they brought Joseph to Pharaoh,
And Joseph said to him,
"Your dreams are from God, He is warning you.
There are important things you need to do!

"There are going to be seven years of plenty,
And Egypt will have
Lots of good healthy food.
But then, a famine will come to the land.
The Lord God wants you to understand.

"There will be seven years with no food in Egypt,
    You need to build barns
        And start saving your food!
            If you work hard, and get this job done,
                Your people won't go hungry,
                    You can feed everyone."

Pharaoh could see that Joseph spoke the truth.
He said, "I can tell that your God is with you.
Your God has helped you understand."
Then he put his ring on Joseph's hand!

Pharaoh gave Joseph jewelry and clothes.
He put Joseph in charge of Egypt's food.
He gave him a horse, and a chariot too!
He told his people, "Do whatever Joseph tells you to do."

For seven years Joseph worked hard.
Pharaoh made Joseph his right-hand man.
Joseph got married and had two sons.
Everything happened just as God had planned!

Joseph showed the people how to save food,
And during the seven years of plenty,
All over Egypt they stored their food,
Because they knew the famine was coming soon.

JOSEPH FORGIVES

Genesis 42-46

After seven years of plenty,
Famine came to all the land.
But the people in Egypt had plenty of food,
Because Pharaoh was following Joseph's plan!

Jacob and his sons lived far away in Canaan,
But the famine had come to their country too.
Jacob told his sons, "You must go to Egypt,
And see if they will sell food to you.

"But Benjamin, my youngest son,
Must stay here with me.
He is too young to go so far."
So, the ten brothers left immediately.

Now, Joseph was governor of Egypt
When the brothers came and bowed down to him.
They did not recognize Joseph, their brother,
But Joseph recognized them!

Joseph said, "I think maybe you are all spies."
The brothers said, "No! We just want to buy grain.
We are 12 brothers from the same family,
We all have the same family name.

"Our youngest brother is home with our father.
We also had a brother who was lost."
Then Joseph spoke sternly, "*If* that is true,
Go and get your youngest brother,
Then I might believe you!

"One of you must stay in Egypt,
He can stay here in our jail.
So, the brothers returned home, but Simeon stayed.
Simeon stayed in the jail.

When the brothers got home, they told their father
All the things that had happened to them.
Jacob did not want Benjamin to go,
He kept on saying, "No! No! No!"
But finally, he decided to let his youngest son go.

"You had better take good care of him!
I wouldn't do this, but we really need food!
Don't let Benjamin out of your sight!
No matter what, make sure he's alright!"

So, the brothers took Benjamin to Egypt,
Where Joseph had prepared a meal for them.
When Joseph entered the room, and sat down in his chair,
All the brothers bowed down to him.

Joseph asked them, "How is your father?
Is he still alive? How has he been?"
"Our father is well," the brothers told him.
Then the brothers bowed down to Joseph again.

Joseph looked up,
He saw his youngest brother.
He remembered that both of them
Had the same mother!

Joseph quickly got up and left the room,
The brothers didn't know why.
When he was alone Joseph began to weep.
He cried, and he cried, and he cried!

Joseph's servants told each brother where to sit at the table,
They were all seated in the order they were born.
The brothers looked at where each of them sat,
And wondered, "How did the servants know
How to do that?"

The brothers were served their lunch.
The food was the very best.
But Benjamin, who sat at the end of the table,
Was given five times more food than all of the rest!

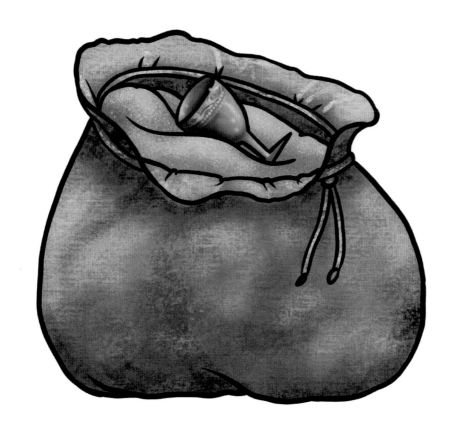

Joseph sold them grain, and sent them on their way.
But he put a silver cup into Benjamin's pack.
He waited awhile, then sent a servant to find them.
And the servant found the silver cup in Benjamin's sack!

"How dare you steal a silver cup,
After we sold our grain to you!"
They took the brothers back to Joseph,
To see what Joseph would do.

"The boy will stay with me," said Joseph,
"The rest of you should quickly leave my sight!"
The brothers panicked, "If Benjamin stays,
What will our father say?"

Judah told Joseph, "We cannot leave Benjamin!
This is going to make our father sick inside!
If Benjamin does not return with us,
I know that our father will surely die!

"You see, our father has already lost a son.
Our brother, Joseph, was his favorite one!"

Then Joseph began to cry.
He sent his servants away.
He told his brothers, "I am Joseph."
Then his brothers were really afraid!

But Joseph told them, "Do not fear!
You weren't the ones who sent me here.
It was God who brought me to Egypt."
Then he hugged his brothers and dried his tears.

"Hurry and bring my father to me!
Bring cousins, and uncles, and their animals too!
Bring everyone here! There is lots of good land!
But please hurry, as fast as you can!"

And that's how God brought His people to Egypt!
The brothers had families, and before very long,
Even though the brothers had done what was wrong,
God's people made homes and settled down in Egypt,
Right where God wanted them. Right where they belonged!

BABY MOSES

Exodus 1-2

After many years in Egypt,
Joseph and his brothers grew old and died.
Then a new Pharaoh came into power,
He was mean, and bossy, and full of pride!

The Pharaoh complained to his people,
"There are too many Hebrews living in my land!

Let's make them our slaves, so they'll understand
That I'm in charge of Egypt! . . . And,

"While we're at it, tell my army
Not to make too much noise.
But I want them to go, and make sure that we kill
All the Hebrew baby boys!"

Now Amram and Jochebed had 3 children,
Miriam, Aaron, and a brand-new baby boy.
They were Hebrews, God's people, they lived in Egypt,
And their children gave them a lot of love and joy.

Miriam and Aaron liked to play with their baby.
They knew to be careful when the soldiers were near.
For three months they hid their baby in their house,
"Shhhh little baby, be quiet as a mouse!"

But as the little baby grew,
He began to make more and more noise.
The baby would laugh, or fuss, or cry,
And if the soldiers were standing nearby,
The family knew their baby could die!

Jochebed made a little basket,
She made the basket waterproof.
She told her children, "I have made a plan,
And it's very important that you understand.

"We're going to hide our baby in this basket.
We will put him in the river where the tall bulrushes grow.
Miriam, I need you to keep watch over our baby,
If something happens you must quickly let me know!"

Before too long, the Pharaoh's daughter came along.
She saw the little basket floating not too far away.
She told her servant, "Go and get that little basket!"
The servant quickly obeyed.

The Princess opened the basket, and saw the crying baby.
"Ohh! It's a Hebrew baby!" the Princess sweetly said.
"But I won't let my father kill **this** little baby!
This baby will be mine instead!"

Miriam was watching and listening,
She ran up to the Princess and said,
"Would you like for me to find a nurse for the baby?
I think that this baby needs to be fed."

The Princess said, "Yes, go find someone for me!"
So, Miriam ran and got her mother.
The Princess said, "I will pay you generously,
If you take him to your home and take care of him for me."
And of course, Jochebed quickly agreed.

The Princess said, "I will name him Moses,
It means 'I drew him out of the water'.
And I won't let anyone harm this baby,
Not even my father!

"I am the Princess! I am Pharaoh's daughter!
There is not any one
Who would dare to hurt this baby,
Because Moses is now my son!"

God had a special plan for baby Moses,
Amram and Jochebed had their baby home with them.
Moses grew up with his brother and sister,
They knew God would always take care of him.

As Moses grew he would go to the palace.
His family loved him, and the Princess loved him too!
God took care of Moses.

Will you trust God to take care of you?
Bow you head and tell Him if you do!

THE BURNING BUSH

Exodus 2-4

One day when Moses had grown up,
He saw Pharaoh's soldier beating a Hebrew man.

It made him so angry that he killed that soldier,
Then he buried him in the sand!

But, there were some people who were watching,
And Moses became afraid.
He knew Pharaoh would kill him, he had no doubt.
So, he ran away to Midian, before Pharaoh could find out.

In Midian, Moses met seven sisters
Who were taking care of their father's sheep.
When some robbers came, Moses protected all of them,
The girl's father was very happy with him!

Moses stayed with that family for many years,
He married one of the daughters.
He had two sons, and grew old, he was enjoying his life
Taking care of his sons and his wife.

One day, while he was taking care of the sheep,
He saw something that looked very odd.
A bush was on fire, but the bush did not burn,
Moses went closer, to see what he could learn.

Then Moses heard the voice of God.
God said, "MOSES, TAKE OFF YOUR SHOES.
YOU ARE STANDING ON HOLY GROUND."
Moses hid his face and looked down.

And although it sounds a little bit odd,
The Bible tells us that Moses was afraid to look at God!

God said, "I HAVE HEARD THE CRIES OF MY PEOPLE,
AND I HAVE A JOB I WANT YOU TO DO.
GO AND TELL PHARAOH TO LET MY PEOPLE GO!
DON'T BE AFRAID, I WILL BE WITH YOU!"

Then Moses said,
"God are you sure that You want me?
There is so much about You that I don't even know!
Who am I, that I should go?

"I don't know what I should say,
And Your people won't believe me, anyway!
I am not a man of great fame,
I don't even know Your name!"

God said to Moses, "**I AM** WHO **I AM**!
I AM THE GOD OF ABRAHAM
TELL MY PEOPLE THAT I HAVE A PLAN,
I'M TAKING THEM TO THE PROMISED LAND!"

Moses told God. "I know they won't listen!
They'll never believe that God spoke to me."
God said, "WHAT'S IN YOUR HAND?"
Moses said, "It's a rod,"
"THROW THE ROD DOWN ON THE GROUND," said God.

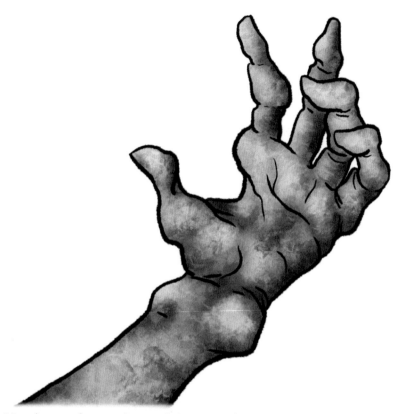

He threw down the rod, it turned into a snake!
Moses was afraid, and tried to run away.
But the Lord said to Moses, "PICK IT UP BY THE TAIL.
I WANT MY PEOPLE TO KNOW
THAT THEIR GOD IS REAL!"
So, Moses slowly reached out his hand,
And then he caught the snake by the tail.
When he did, the snake turned back into a rod!
"NOW PUT YOUR HAND INSIDE YOUR SHIRT," said God.

Moses obeyed, and when he pulled out his hand,
It was full of leprosy, as white as snow!
So, he put his hand back in his shirt, and then,
His hand became healthy and strong again!

Moses told God, "I'm not a good speaker."
God asked Moses, "WHO MADE YOUR MOUTH?
TELL ME, WHO MADE YOUR EARS AND YOUR EYES?"
The Lord said to Moses, "IS IT NOT I?

"NOW GO, AND I WILL BE YOUR MOUTH.
I WILL TEACH YOU WHAT TO SAY."
But Moses said, "Please! Send someone else!"
Moses did not want to obey.
And God was angry with Moses that day.

God said "I'LL SEND YOUR BROTHER AARON WITH YOU.
HE'S A GOOD SPEAKER AND HE WILL BE YOUR MOUTH,
BUT I WILL TEACH YOU WHAT TO SAY AND DO.
THEN, YOU CAN TELL AARON WHAT I HAVE TOLD YOU.
AND BE SURE TO TAKE YOUR ROD WITH YOU!

"NOW, GO TO EGYPT, THE PHARAOH HAS DIED.
A NEW PHARAOH IS IN CHARGE OF THE LAND!"
So, Moses took his wife and his sons,
And went to Egypt, just as God had planned.

THE TEN PLAGUES
Exodus 6-12

After God spoke to Moses from the burning bush,
After God tells Moses, "THERE'S A JOB FOR YOU TO DO",
After Moses tells God, "Please send someone else!",
God tells Moses, "I AM SENDING YOU.
BUT YOUR BROTHER, AARON, MAY GO WITH YOU, TOO."

So, Moses and Aaron went to Egypt.
They told Pharaoh, "Let God's people go!"
But Pharaoh just laughed at Moses and said,
"I don't know your God, and I will not let them go.

"Do you think you can tell *me* what to do?
I'm the Pharaoh, and Egypt belongs to me!
In fact, I think I'll make them work harder!"
Then he beat them, and treated them terribly.
Pharaoh told Moses, "Your God can't boss me!"

Moses told God, "The Pharaoh won't listen,
And he will not let Your people go."
God said, "DON'T WORRY, I HAVE A PLAN.
I'M GOING TO BRING MY PEOPLE
TO THE PROMISED LAND.
EGYPT, AND THE PHARAOH, WILL SOON UNDERSTAND,
WHEN I STRETCH OUT MY POWERFUL HAND."

And that is exactly what the Lord God did.
He told Moses, "TAKE YOUR ROD,
AND STRETCH OUT YOUR HAND."
Then Egypt's rivers and streams turned to BLOOD!
There was blood in the water and all through the land.

Moses told Pharaoh, "Let God's people go!"
But the Pharaoh just said, "No! No! No!"

So . . . God sent the **FROGS** to Egypt.
They came into the houses and they jumped on the beds!
There were frogs everywhere! Moses said,
"Let God's people go!"

Pharaoh said, "OK!
Just get these frogs out of my way!"
But then he changed his mind,
And he would *not* let them go!

So . . .God sent the plague of **GNATS**.

God sent the plague of FLIES.

God sent the plague of SICK ANIMALS.
Pharaoh's people complained, and cried.

But Pharaoh's heart was hard, he said,
"Go get Moses and let him know
The Hebrews are my slaves,
And I will NOT let them go!"

So . . . God sent the plague of **BOILS**.
There were terrible sores on the Egyptians' skin.

Then HAIL STONES hit the Egyptians on the head.
And after each plague the Pharaoh said,
"OK! I'll let the Hebrews go!"
Then he would change his mind.
He kept telling Moses, "No! No! No!
I do not want to let my slaves go!"

So . . . God sent the LOCUSTS.
They filled up the houses,
They got in their faces.
There were millions of locusts,
In all kinds of places!

They ate up the trees,
They ate up the plants,
They got in their clothes,
And crawled up their pants!

But foolish Pharaoh kept changing his mind.
His heart was hard. He told Moses, "No!
I am the Pharaoh, and Egypt is *MY* land.
I will not let the people go!"

So . . . God sent the **DARKNESS**.
For three long days they could not see.
First Pharaoh said, "Go!"
Then he said, "No!"
Then he told Moses, "Stay away from me!

"I am the Pharaoh! Get out of here!
I don't want to see your face anymore!
No more games and no more plagues!"
But the Lord told Moses, "THERE **WILL** BE **ONE** MORE.

"I'M GOING TO SEND THE PLAGUE OF **DEATH.**
IN EVERY EGYPTIAN FAMILY, SOMEONE WILL DIE.
THEN PHARAOH WILL UNDERSTAND,
AND HE WILL KNOW
THAT HE *MUST* LET MY PEOPLE GO!

"TELL MY PEOPLE TO GET READY,
DEATH IS COMING TO EGYPT TONIGHT.
AND DEATH WILL *PASS OVER*
THE HOUSES OF MY PEOPLE
WHO DO WHAT IS RIGHT IN MY SIGHT.

"THEY MUST PUT BLOOD ON THEIR DOORPOSTS,
THEN GO INSIDE AND EAT A SPECIAL DINNER.
EARLY IN THE MORNING, THEY MUST BE READY TO GO.
THIS IS A DAY I WANT THEM TO ALWAYS REMEMBER!"

And it all happened just as the Lord God said,
Death came to Egypt that night.
Pharaoh finally told Moses, "OK!
Just get all of God's people out of my way!"

Finally, God's people left Egypt.
Finally, they were free, and not slaves any more.
Moses led them, carrying his rod,
Thousands of people who belonged to God.

LEAVING EGYPT

Exodus 13-15

Moses was a humble man,
He lived in Egypt long ago.
God had a job for Moses:
"GO TELL PHARAOH TO *LET MY PEOPLE GO!*"

But when Moses told Pharaoh what God had said,
Pharaoh's face turned angry and red.
"These people are my slaves," he said,
"I certainly will *not* let them go!"

So, God sent the plagues to Egypt,
And when God finally sent the plague of **DEATH**,
The Pharaoh told Moses, "Get away from me!
Get God's people and go! Immediately!"

So, they started for the Promised Land.
How would they get there? It seemed so far away!
Then Moses made a speech and told all the people,
"Forever we must remember this day.
Our God has rescued us, He will show us the way!"

With a cloud by day, and a fire by night,
The Lord God led His people.
Thousands of children, and women, and men,
And all of their sheep, and cattle, with them.

But back in Egypt the wicked Pharaoh
Changed his mind again!
He told his army, "Get ready to attack!
We're going to bring those people back!"

Just as God's people got to the Red Sea,
They heard Pharaoh's army coming!
There was no place for the people to go!
What would they do? They did not know!

The Red Sea was in front of them,
The Pharaoh was behind them.
They did not want to go back to Egypt,
They did not want to be slaves!
They wanted to live in peace with their families,
They were frightened, and they did not feel brave.

Then the Lord God did a miracle,
Because he loves His people.
The Lord said to Moses, "LIFT UP YOUR ROD!
STRETCH OUT YOUR HAND – **I AM** THE LORD GOD!"

So, Moses stretched his hand, and his rod
Out over the sea.
The waters of the sea divided!
The people hurried through, immediately!

As the people walked through, they could feel and see
That the ground beneath them was dry as could be!
And the water around them was like a wall,
It stood up on each side, strong and tall!

When the very last person made it through,
The Lord closed up the sea.
Pharaoh's chariots and his army
Were chasing God's people,
But they were all drowned, immediately.

Then the people shouted to the Lord!
They sang, "Praise God we are free!
Our God has triumphed gloriously!
Our God has given us victory!"

So, you see God loved these people.
He took good care of them.
With a cloud by day and a fire by night,
His people followed Him.

They were on their way to the Promised Land,
Just as God had planned!

GRUMBLING IN THE DESERT

Exodus 16-17

Do you remember how Moses told Pharaoh,
"Let God's people GO!"?
And even when God sent the plagues,
Pharaoh kept on saying, "No!"?

Finally, Pharaoh told Moses,
"Get God's people out of here!"
So, they started for the Promised Land,
Moses was their leader.

They had to stop when they reached the Red Sea,
Pharaoh's army was chasing them!
Foolish Pharaoh had changed his mind,
And he wanted his slaves back again.

Do you remember what God did next?
He did a miracle, and He opened up the sea!
All of God's people walked safely through,
Pharaoh's army was drowned, immediately.

Then, did God leave them alone in the desert?
No, of course not! God had a plan.
There was a place, far, far away,
It was called the Promised Land.

With a cloud by day, and a fire by night,
The Lord God guided them.
Surely these people would never forget
The great miracles God had done for them.

But, on their way to the Promised Land,
The people began to grumble.
They complained about this . . .
They complained about that . . .
Mumble, bumble, grumble.

"We should have stayed in Egypt."
"We will probably die from the heat!"
"Moses, you brought us into the desert,
But we're tired, and we have aching feet!"

"We don't like it here, and we're hungry."
"Traveling is such a big mess!"
"We don't even know where the Promised Land is!"
"We'll probably starve to death."

Moses went to the Lord and said,
"The people are mad as can be."
God told Moses, "THEY'RE NOT MAD AT YOU,
THE PEOPLE ARE GRUMBLING AGAINST ME."

But God loved His people, and He had a plan,
He told Moses, "JUST WATCH, AND SEE WHAT I'LL DO!
THE PEOPLE WILL HAVE PLENTY OF FOOD TO EAT,
I WILL RAIN BREAD FROM HEAVEN FOR YOU!

"IN THE EVENING, YOU'LL EAT MEAT.
IN THE MORNING, YOU'LL EAT BREAD.
AND THEN EVERYONE WILL KNOW FOR SURE
THAT I AM YOUR GOD."

So, Moses told the people, "Stop your complaining.
God always provides for you, and for me!
I'm just a man, but God is our leader.
You're grumbling against God, can't you see?"

That evening, quail came and covered the camp.
In the morning, guess what they found?
Little flakes that tasted like honey
Were lying all over the ground.

The people asked Moses, "What is this?"
Moses said, "It is our bread and our meat.
The Lord has sent it to us,
So we will have plenty to eat!"

The people called the little flakes Manna.
They gathered it up in the morning.
They cooked it like mush, they baked it like bread.
God took care of His people, just as Moses had said.

But then those people began again!
Mumble, bumble, grumble.
"We're all going to die! Oh dear! Oh dear!"
"We are thirsty and there is no water out here!"

But God had plan, and He told Moses,
"YOU MUST DO EXACTLY WHAT I SAY TO DO.
PICK UP YOUR STAFF, AND STRIKE THE ROCK,
THERE WILL BE ENOUGH WATER FOR ALL OF YOU."

So, Moses did as the Lord told him,
And water came out, just as God said!
Will these people ever learn to trust and obey?
Will they keep forgetting God has shown them the way?

As they traveled, there were many more things
That happened to the people of God,
As they were going to the Promised Land,
Led by Moses, carrying his rod.

THE TEN COMMANDMENTS
Exodus 19-20

They were on their way to the Promised Land
When they entered the wilderness.
They camped at the bottom of Mt. Sinai,
To spend a few days, to eat and to rest.

The Lord God called to Moses from the mountain,
"REMIND MY PEOPLE OF WHAT I HAVE DONE,
I BROUGHT YOU OUT OF EGYPT,
I AM GOD, THE HOLY ONE.

AND YOU ARE MY PEOPLE,
YOU MUST OBEY ONLY ME."
So Moses told this to the people,
And the people said, "We all agree!
We will follow God faithfully."

Then the Lord spoke to Moses and said,
"I AM COMING TO YOU IN A CLOUD.
I WANT YOU TO COME TO ME ON THE MOUNTAIN
LISTEN CAREFULLY, AND I'LL TELL YOU HOW.

"MY PEOPLE MUST STAY
AT THE BOTTOM OF THE MOUNTAIN,
I AM GOING TO MEET ONLY WITH YOU."
When Moses got to the bottom of Mt. Sinai,
There was thunder, and lightning too!
The people stood at the bottom of the mountain,
They could hear a horn, and the mountain began to shake.
Smoke filled the mountain and the sky,
Moses spoke to God, and God thundered His reply.

When Moses came down from the mountain,
He showed the people the Ten Commandments.
He said, "These are the things God wants us to do.
These are God's words for me and for you."

"I AM THE LORD YOUR GOD.
I BROUGHT YOU OUT OF EGYPT.
I RESCUED YOU FROM SLAVERY.
HAVE NO OTHER GOD BEFORE ME.

"DO NOT MAKE OR WORSHIP IDOLS,
YOU MUST WORSHIP ONLY ME.
DO NOT USE MY NAME FOR EVIL.
KEEP THE SEVENTH DAY HOLY
AND WORSHIP FAITHFULLY.

"HONOR YOUR FATHER AND MOTHER.
DO NOT MURDER OR KILL.
BE TRUE TO THE ONE YOU MARRY.
DO NOT STEAL.

"DON'T TELL LIES ABOUT OTHER PEOPLE.
DON'T BE WISHING FOR OTHER PEOPLE'S THINGS."

So, these were the Ten Commandments
That God gave to Moses that day.
God told Moses, "TELL THE PEOPLE
THEY MUST LISTEN AND OBEY."

God wrote the Ten Commandments on a tablet of stone,
So Moses could teach the people.
We can read these commandments today, because
They're written in the Bible in the Book of Exodus.

But the people did not obey Gods laws.
So God sent Jesus His only Son.
Jesus would die for the sins of His people,
To forgive us for the wrongs we have done.

Thank You God for the Bible.
Thank You for Jesus, Your Son.
Thank You for forgiving me,
You are my God, the Holy One.

JOSHUA AND CALEB

Numbers 13-14

God brought His people out of Egypt,
Out of slavery.
He saved them from the Pharaoh,
They walked through the Red Sea.

They traveled safely through the desert,
Just as God had planned.
And now they were finally
At the Promised Land.

They chose 12 men, one from each tribe,
To go and spy out the land.
The grapes were big, there was lots of good food,
The city was beautiful and grand!

Ten of the spies told the people,
"The enemy's army is large and strong.
We don't think that we should fight them,
Maybe God was wrong.

"If we go into their land, they will kill us.
They are giants, they are powerful and strong!
We think we should go back to Egypt,
That's where we belong."

But two of the spies told the people,
"We can do it if we try!
We know the Lord is with us,
We know God is by our side."

Yes, Joshua and Caleb
Knew just what to do!
They said to all the people,
"God will take care of you.

"The Lord our God will keep us safe.
We must trust Him -- do not fear."
But the people told Moses, "We are afraid!
Let's get out of here!"

God told Moses, "MY PEOPLE DON'T TRUST ME.
SO, I WANT YOU TO UNDERSTAND,
THE ONES WHO REFUSE TO LISTEN TO ME
WILL NOT ENTER THE PROMISED LAND.

"I HAVE HEARD THEIR COMPLAINING.
I HAVE HEARD THEM TALK ABOUT THEIR FEARS.
I'M SENDING THEM BACK
TO WANDER IN THE WILDERNESS
FOR 40 MORE YEARS.

"THE COMPLAINERS WILL DIE IN THE WILDERNESS.
THEN, I'LL BRING THEIR CHILDREN
BACK TO THE PROMISED LAND.
JOSHUA AND CALEB WILL ALSO RETURN.
THERE IS A LESSON THAT MY PEOPLE MUST LEARN."

So, when you feel afraid,
Remember, God is near.
Don't complain, and don't forget,
And do not fear!
We don't have to be afraid,
Because our God is here!

JERICHO – THE PROMISED LAND

Joshua 1-6

After Moses grew old and died,
The Lord told Joshua, "THIS IS MY PLAN:
JOSHUA, YOU WILL LEAD MY PEOPLE
INTO THE PROMISED LAND.

"I WILL GIVE YOU VICTORY,
I'LL SHOW YOU WHAT TO DO.
I WAS WITH MOSES,
AND I WILL BE WITH YOU!"

Just across the river
Was the city of Jericho.
So, Joshua chose two spies and said,
"It's time for you to go.
See how strong the city is,
Come back, and let me know."

So, the spies snuck into the city,
To have a look inside.
"**Who's there?**" yelled out a soldier.
The spies ran off to hide!

"Come up here! I will help you,"
They heard a woman call.
They quickly went inside her house,
Which was high on the city wall.

"You men must hide," the woman said,
Rahab was her name,
"Go to the roof, I'll hide you there!
I am so glad you came.

"The people here are all afraid,
They don't know who you are.
But I know God is on your side,
He brought you from afar."

She hid them on the rooftop
Until the soldiers passed.

Then brought them down and said to them,
"You'll have to leave here fast!

"I'll lower the basket down the wall,
And leave the red rope to show
That I was the one who helped God's people.
When you capture the city, please let my family go."

The men told Rahab, "We'll do as you say,
We make this promise, and we all agree.
But don't forget to leave the red rope,
So our people will know that you should go free."

The spies ran back to Joshua and said,
"The Promised Land is great!
Let's do whatever God says to do,
We are ready to obey."

Then the Lord spoke to Joshua,
"THIS IS WHAT I SAY,
GO MARCH AROUND THE CITY OF JERICHO
ONE TIME EVERY DAY.

"ONLY THE PRIESTS WILL BLOW THEIR TRUMPETS,
NO ONE ELSE SHOULD MAKE A SOUND.
THEN ON THE SEVENTH DAY,
MARCH SEVEN TIMES AROUND!"

So, they did as the Lord commanded,
And for 6 days they quietly marched around.

Then on the 7th day,
They marched seven times around.
Then Joshua commanded the people to **SHOUT!**
And the walls of Jericho came tumbling down!

Rahab and her family were saved!
And now everyone could see God's plan.
His people were safely out of Egypt.
They had finally arrived at the Promised Land!

GIDEON

Judges 6-8

Moses led them out of Egypt,
Just as God had planned.
And now they were finally
At the Promised Land.

God had rescued them from slavery.
They were finally safe and free.
They built their homes and prayed to God,
They lived together happily!

But after a while . . .

The people began to forget about God,
They did bad things, and they sinned a lot.
So, for seven years God allowed
The army of Midian to rule over them.

The army of Midian was mean and rude.
They stole the people's animals,
They took away their food.

God's people were afraid.
They tried to run and hide from them.
But they just could not get away
From the army of Midian.

Finally, God's people cried out to Him,
"Please, save us from the army of Midian!"
And even though His people
Had sinned and disobeyed Him,
God sent an angel to a man named Gideon.

The angel sat under an old oak tree,
Gideon was as busy as he could be.
The angel spoke, "The Lord is with you
Mighty warrior man,
And God will use you to save His people from Midian!"

But Gideon asked the angel,
"Are sure that God wants me?
I'm not rich, and I'm not important.
Why would God choose me?"

But God never makes a mistake.
And the angel told Gideon, "The Lord will be with you."
So finally, Gideon said to the angel,
"I will do whatever God wants me to do."

Gideon blew his trumpet,
To call out all of God's men.
But the Lord told Gideon,
"THERE ARE TOO MANY.
YOU DON'T NEED 32,000 OF THEM.

"I WANT MY PEOPLE TO KNOW
IT'S NOT BY THEIR OWN POWER THAT THEY WILL WIN.
I WILL USE ONLY A FEW OF THESE MEN,
AND THEY WILL WIN BECAUSE I AM WITH THEM.

"SEND AWAY THE MEN WHO DON'T WANT TO FIGHT,
SEND AWAY ALL THE MEN WHO ARE WEAK.
SEND AWAY THE MEN WHO LAP WATER LIKE A PUP,
KEEP ONLY THE ONES
THAT USE THEIR HANDS LIKE A CUP."

After Gideon sent all these men home,
He had an army of only 300 men.
The Midianite army was in the valley below,
There were thousands and thousands
And thousands of them!

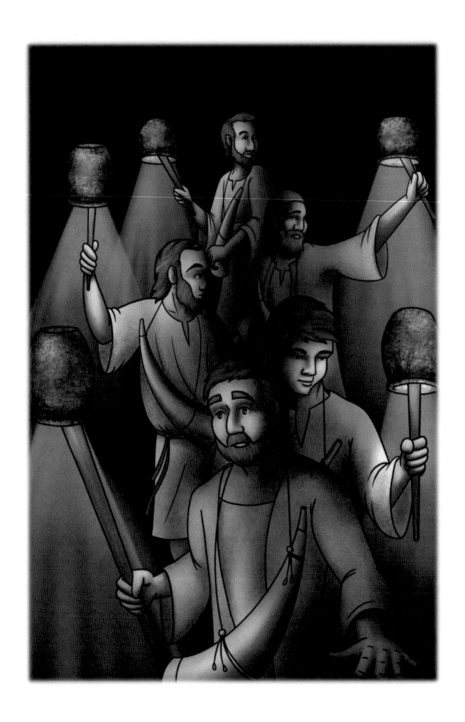

"Follow me, and do just as I do.
Be very quiet," Gideon told his men.
They waited until it was dark and very still.
The Midianite army slept in tents down the hill.

Gideon's small army of 300 men
Put jars over torches and waited . . . and then,
All of a sudden, Gideon gave a loud shout.
They broke their jars and waved their fire about!

They blew their horns and made lots of noise,
They shouted and ran around here and there!
The Midianites woke up, confused and scared,
There were fires and noises everywhere!

The bad guys ran around,
Confused by all the sound.
They finally ran away.
God saved His people! Hip-hip, hooray!

Then the people spoke to Gideon,
"Please rule over us. You saved us from Midian."
But Gideon told them, "I'm not a fool.
No, I will not rule.
The **Lord** will rule over you!"

SAMPSON

Judges 13-16

Even before Samson was born
His life was in God's care.
God told Samson's mom and dad,
"DO NOT CUT HIS HAIR."

As Samson grew, he obeyed the Lord,
God made Samson extra strong.
One day something amazing happened
As Samson was walking along.

An angry lion jumped out to attack,
But the Lord was with Samson, and so
Although the lion fought with all his might,
Samson was stronger, and he won the fight!

Now the Philistines were the enemies of God's people.
They hated Samson, they tied him up with rope.
But God gave Samson special strength that day,
And Samson had the power to get away!

Then Samson picked up a dried up old bone,
And began to fight the men.
By the end of the day, those men were killed,
Samson had won his fight again!

This made the Philistines really mad.
They made a plan to capture Samson.
"Tomorrow we will meet him at the city's gate."
The Philistines were filled with hate.

But Samson heard about their plan
He didn't make a sound.
Late that night he went to the gate,
And tore it right out of the ground!

Then he carried that big old gate
Up to the top of a hill.
So, when his enemies met the next day,
Samson was gone -- far, far away.
And so was their city gate.
Samson had tricked them again!

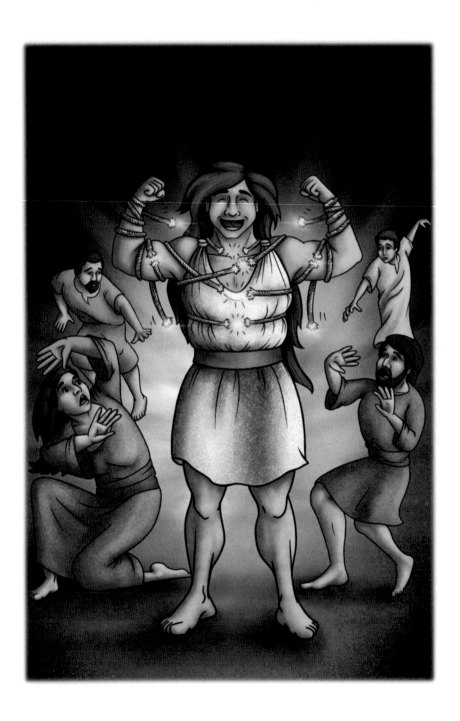

Now, Samson loved a woman,
Delilah was her name.
The Philistines came to talk to her,
"Please play our little game.

"We'll give you lots of money,
All you have to do,
Is find out the secret of Samson's strength,
We'll tell you what to do."

The very next day, Delilah said,
"Samson, please tell me true,
Why are you stronger than anyone else?
Why can't your enemies capture you?"

Samson decided to trick Delilah.
He said, "I'll tell you what to do.
Brand new rope is stronger than me."
But Samson was teasing, and that wasn't true.

Delilah said, "Let's play a game.
Let me tie your hands and feet."
But Samson was stronger than any rope,
And he snapped them off easily.

Day after day Delilah teased him
With her silly games.
But Samson would not tell her
The secret to his power and fame.

Then finally one day,
Samson told his secret.
"God told me that my hair should grow,
If I cut my hair, my strength will surely go."

And so that night as Samson slept
Peacefully on his bed,
Delilah called the Philistines,
Who quickly shaved his head.

Samson awoke and saw his enemies,
But when he stood up to fight,
His hair was gone, and so was his strength.
The power of God had left him that night.
Samson's tricking and teasing had not turned out right.

The Philistines captured Samson,
And they were not kind.
Day after day they tortured him,
They poked out his eyes, so he was blind.

Life for Samson was very hard.
But his enemies did not know,
That as the days were passing,
Samson's hair began to grow.

One day at a party,
The Philistines laughed, "Bring Samson here.
He used to be strong but now he is not,
We have no reason to fear."

They put Samson between two pillars,
And everyone went outside.
They wanted to tease and laugh at Samson,
Samson turned his face to the sky.

"O Lord God, remember me,"
Samson began to pray,
"Please give me strength just one more time,
Then let me end my days."

And God heard Samson's prayer
He gave Samson back his strength.
Then Samson pushed the temple down,
And killed the Philistines!

Samson died that day,
But someday I hope I will see,
Samson, the strongest man in the world
In heaven with Jesus, and you, and me!

 Ginny Lowe began teaching Sunday School when she was just 12 years old. This is the book she would have liked to have had when she started teaching. All the people Ginny writes about in these Bible stories were on a journey, and it is amazing to see what God did to help them. Ginny has spent a lifetime teaching God's Word to children. Ask her before her class which is her favorite Bible story and the answer is almost always the one she is teaching today. The children shown on the cover represent the seven children God gave to Ginny and her husband, Keith. They are on a journey too - just like you. Ginny and Keith live in their family home in Gresham, Oregon.

Cathy Rowe is a children's book illustrator working out of Oregon City, OR. She grew up in California and graduated from Cal Poly, San Luis Obispo with a BFA in Studio Art in 2007. Since moving to Oregon with her husband and young daughter, Cathy has been passionate about children's illustration as a way to inspire children to learn, think, wonder, and make good choices. Cathy published her first book, *Explore ABC Fun: An Assembled Alphabet Adventure*, in 2018. To see more information about this book and Cathy's other illustration projects go to www.CathyRowe.com .

Made in the USA
Lexington, KY
21 November 2019